MOONBEAM
IS LOST

SELMA AND JACK
WASSERMANN

ILLUSTRATIONS
GEORGE ROHRER

BENEFIC PRESS
WESTCHESTER, ILLINOIS

The Moonbeam Books

MOONBEAM

MOONBEAM IS CAUGHT

MOONBEAM AND THE CAPTAIN

MOONBEAM AT THE ROCKET PORT

MOONBEAM AND THE ROCKET RIDE

MOONBEAM AND DAN STARR

MOONBEAM FINDS A MOON STONE

MOONBEAM AND SUNNY

MOONBEAM AND THE BIG JUMP

MOONBEAM IS LOST

Edited by
Joellen Reiter

Contents

Moonbeam Alone

Here are Scott and Dr. Jim.

They work at the Rocket Port with Moonbeam the chimp.

The men are looking for Moonbeam.

Where can she be?

"Oh! There you are," said Scott.

"Soon you are going to the moon, chimp," said Dr. Jim.

"We are going to help you."

"Come. We have work to do," Scott said.

But Moonbeam did not come.

"What is the
trouble, Moonbeam?"
said Scott.

"You will not get
to the moon this way."

"I will have a
look at the chimp,"
said Dr. Jim.

"Then we will see."

Dr. Jim looked
at Moonbeam.

He looked her up
and down.

Soon Dr. Jim looked up.

"I can not find the trouble,"
he said.

Scott looked at Moonbeam.

"What will we do with you?"
he asked.

Then Dr. Jim looked at Scott.

"Moonbeam is all alone here," he said.

"No other chimps are at the Rocket Port."

"That could be the trouble," said Scott.

"She wants to be with other chimps.

But what can we do to help her?"

"I know," said Scott, and he
jumped up.

"We can find a friend for her!
Come on, you two."

And out he ran.

"What is he up to?" said Dr. Jim.

"Hon? Hon, hon?" said Moonbeam.

And they went out after Scott.

"Jump in," said Scott.

Dr. Jim jumped in with Moonbeam.

"Where are we going?" Dr. Jim said.

"You will see," said Scott.

Scott and Dr. Jim and Moonbeam
went fast.

Soon they were out of the
Rocket Port.

Mr. Long

On and on they went.
Then Scott stopped.
"Here we are," he said.
They were at the zoo.

"Now I know," said Dr. Jim.

"This is where we can find a
friend for Moonbeam."

"Hon? Hon?" said Moonbeam.

"Come on, Moonbeam," said Scott.

"We will look for chimps."

Moonbeam went into the zoo with
Scott and Dr. Jim.

The men looked for chimps.

"What a big zoo this is," said Scott.

"Where can the chimps be?"

Moonbeam looked this way and
that way.

She saw no friends here.

Moonbeam and the two men went on.
Then Dr. Jim said, "Look!"
They saw that they could go
two ways.

"This way," said Scott.

But Moonbeam did
not want to go
that way.

She went the
other way.

The two men ran
after her.

CHIMP GIRAFFE

Soon they came
to something big.
It was Mr. Long.
Moonbeam had to
look way, way up
to see all
of him.

Moonbeam looked
and looked at
Mr. Long.
"Hoon! Hon!"
she laughed.

Mr. Long

Moonbeam liked
Mr. Long.

And Mr. Long
liked her.

He came down to
have a good look
at her.

Then Dr. Jim
said, "Look
at that!"

Mr. Long was
going up, and
Moonbeam was
going up with him.

Up and up went
Moonbeam and
her friend.

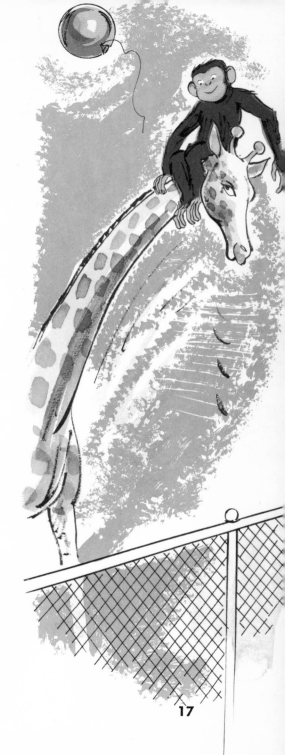

Scott looked up.
"Come down,
Moonbeam," he said.
"Hoon! Hoon!"
said Moonbeam.

"Come down, and we will look
for chimps," said Scott.

Moonbeam came down.

She looked back at her friend,
Mr. Long.

Then she went with Scott
and Dr. Jim.

"Look, Moonbeam," said Dr. Jim.

Moonbeam looked.

She saw the chimps.

"Hoon! Hoon!" she said.

The other chimps looked at her.

"Ung? Ung?" said one chimp.

The chimps looked and looked
at Moonbeam.

"Hoon! Hoon!" said Moonbeam.

"Ung? Ung? Ung?" said all the
other chimps.

Scott laughed.

"They do not know what you are
doing out here, Moonbeam," he said.

"They do not know that you are a
moon chimp."

The Chopper

Scott, Dr. Jim, and Moonbeam came out of the zoo.

"Back to the Rocket Port,"
said Scott.
"And back to work."

"What now?" Dr. Jim wanted to know.

"Now we have to help Moonbeam get lost," said Scott.

"Lost? What for?" asked Dr. Jim.

"Moonbeam could get lost when she is on the moon," said Scott.

"We have to know what she will do.

We have to know if she can find her way."

Scott came to a stop.

"This is the Chopper, Moonbeam,"
he said.

"You will go far, far away in it.

When it comes down, you will
get out.

Then you will have to find your way
back here all alone."

Moonbeam did not know what
Scott wanted.

"Hoon? Hoon?" she said.

"Get in, Moonbeam," said Scott.

Moonbeam got into the Chopper.

She looked out at Scott and Dr. Jim.

The two men looked at Moonbeam.

"You can do it, Moonbeam," said Scott.

"See you soon," said Dr. Jim.

Then the Chopper went up.

"Look at it go!" said Dr. Jim.

Up and away went the Chopper.

The Chopper went on.

Moonbeam looked down.

She could not see the Rocket Port.

It was far away now.

Where was this Chopper going?

Moonbeam did not know.

Soon the Chopper came down.

It came to a stop, and Moonbeam jumped out.

She looked at the Chopper.

But the men did not come out.

Then the Chopper went back up.

Moonbeam ran after it, but she could not get to it.

She was all alone now.

Moonbeam looked
this way and
that way.

It was up to her
to find a way back
to the Rocket Port.
But she did not
know where she was.
"Heen!" said
Moonbeam. "Heen!"

This Way And That Way

Then the Chopper came back.

Moonbeam looked up and saw it.

But the Chopper did not help her.

Moonbeam looked at all the ways that she could go.

One way looked good to her.

She went that way.

Moonbeam went on and on.

And the Chopper went where
Moonbeam went.

Moonbeam could see it when she
looked up.

But the Chopper did not come down
to help her.

Moonbeam was
going fast now.
Then something
was in her way!
But Moonbeam
did not see it.

"Ga-rrrump! Ga-rrrump!"
it went.

Moonbeam jumped back.

"Heeeeeeeen!"
she said.

Then she ran
and ran.

Moonbeam ran on and on.

But she could not go on running
like that.

Soon she could not run at all.

She came to a stop.

Moonbeam looked this way and
that way.

But all she saw was trees.

"Heen! Heen!" said Moonbeam.

She did not know where to go.

"Heen!" Moonbeam said. "Heen!"

She did not know what to do.

Moonbeam was lost.

Moonbeam looked
at all the trees.
Then it came
to her!
She went to one
of the big trees.
And she went up
in the tree.
Up and up and
up she went.

35

Soon Moonbeam was all the way up.

Now she could see where she was.

She looked one way.

No, that was not the way to go.

Then she looked the other way.

Not far away was the zoo.

"Hoon!" said Moonbeam. "Hoon! Hoon!"

Moonbeam could see the way to go now.

It was not the way to the Rocket Port, but Moonbeam liked the zoo.

She was soon on her way down the tree.

When she was all the way down, she ran.

Stop That Chimp!

Moonbeam ran all the way to the zoo.
The Chopper came after her.
The men at the zoo looked
at Moonbeam.

"The moon chimp!" they said.
"What is she doing here all alone?"
Then they looked up and saw
the Chopper.

It was coming down.

Moonbeam ran on.

She wanted to see her friend,

Mr. Long

"Stop!" the men said to Moonbeam.

But Moonbeam did not stop.

"Stop that chimp!" said the men.

Then they ran after her.

Soon Moonbeam saw Mr. Long.
"Hoon! Hoon!" she said.
Mr. Long looked down at Moonbeam.
It was good to see her.

Moonbeam wanted
to be with Mr. Long.
She did not want
the men to get her.
What could
she do?

Then the men came.

"Here she is," they
said. "Stop her!"

Moonbeam looked
at Mr. Long.

She looked at
the men.

"Heen!" she said.

Then she
ran away.

The men ran
after her.

Moonbeam ran, and then she stopped.

She saw the men from the Chopper.

Moonbeam looked this way and
that way.

The men from the zoo were coming
one way.

And the men from the Chopper were
coming the other way.

"Heeeeeen!" said Moonbeam.

Then Moonbeam saw something.

The chimps! That was it!

Moonbeam ran.

She ran fast.

Soon she was in with the
other chimps.

Now she could stop running.

Soon the men came.

They looked at the chimps.

But Moonbeam looked like all the
other chimps.

"Moonbeam, where are you?" asked
the men from the Chopper.

But Moonbeam did not come out.

"I will get help," said one of
the men.

And he went away.

Soon he said, "Is that you, Scott?

Your chimp is here, but we can
not find her.

Can you and Dr. Jim come and help?"

"We are coming," said Scott.

Dr. Jim and Scott were soon at the zoo.

They looked at all the chimps.

"Are you here, Moonbeam?" asked Dr. Jim.

"Be a good chimp, Moonbeam," said Scott.

"Come out."

But Moonbeam did not come out.

Then she said, "Heen! Hon! Hon!" Now the men could see where she was. They laughed and went in after her.

"What will we do
with you?"
said Scott.
"You did not find
your way back to
the Rocket Port,"
said Dr. Jim.

"Heen! Heen!"
said Moonbeam.
Then they went
out of the zoo.

47

Trouble In The Zoo

Dr. Jim, Moonbeam, and Scott were not far away from the zoo when someone said, "Stop!"

It was one of the men from the zoo.

"We have trouble in the zoo," he said.

"Come with me."

Moonbeam and Scott and Dr. Jim went with him.

"Look at this," said the man from the zoo.

"Mr. Long was here, but he is not here now.

Your chimp did this.

She let him out."

"Mr. Long is your friend, Moonbeam," said Scott.

"You will have to help find him."

"We will all help," said Dr. Jim.

The men from the
zoo looked for
Mr. Long.

Scott and Dr. Jim
looked for Mr. Long.

And Moonbeam
looked for Mr. Long.

They looked
and looked.

But Mr. Long was
not in the zoo.

"We will have to
go out of the zoo
to find him," said
one of the men.

They all went out of the zoo.

They looked this way and that way.

But no one saw Mr. Long.

"Where can he be?" asked Scott.

"Hon? Hon?" said Moonbeam.

Dr. Jim and the men from the zoo went one way to look for Mr. Long.

Moonbeam and Scott looked the other way.

But Moonbeam did not see where Scott was going.

When she looked up, she saw that she was all alone.

"Hon?" she said.

But she went on looking for Mr. Long.

Moonbeam looked this way and
that way.

All she saw was trees, trees, trees.
She looked at the trees.

Then she jumped up and down.

A tree had helped her find the way
to the zoo when she was lost.

Could a tree help her find
Mr. Long now?

Moonbeam ran to a big tree.

Up and up the tree she went.

Now she could see far away.

Moonbeam looked and looked.

Then she saw something.

It was Mr. Long!

And far away she saw the
Rocket Port.

"Hoon! Hoon!" said Moonbeam.

And she came down from the tree.

When she was all the way down,
she ran.

Now she could find Mr. Long.

Moonbeam Finds The Way

Mr. Long looked
at the trees.

Something was
coming!

Mr. Long could
not see what
it was.

He did not know
it was Moonbeam.

Away he ran.

Moonbeam ran after Mr. Long.

"Heeeen!" she said. "Heeeen!"

Mr. Long looked back.

It was his friend, the chimp.

Mr. Long stopped running.

"Hoon! Hoon!" said Moonbeam.

Moonbeam ran up to Mr. Long.
She wanted to get back to the
Rocket Port with him.
Mr. Long helped Moonbeam.
Up, up, up she went.

Then away went the two friends.
With Moonbeam's help, Mr. Long
could find the Rocket Port.

Mr. Long was fast.
It was not far to the Rocket Port
for him.

Soon Moonbeam and Mr. Long were at the Rocket Port.

They saw the Chopper coming down.

And they saw Dr. Jim and Scott coming back to the Rocket Port.

"Look!" said Dr. Jim.

"It is Moonbeam and Mr. Long," Scott said.

"See?" said Dr. Jim.

"Moonbeam can find her way.

She did not get lost after all."

Moonbeam was soon down with the
two men.

"Good work, Moonbeam," said Scott.

"Now I can let the zoo know that
Mr. Long is here."

"Hoon! Hoon!" said Moonbeam.

It was good to be back.

The men from the
zoo came to the
Rocket Port.

They saw Moonbeam.

"What a chimp!"
they said.

"She will be good
to have on
the moon.

When something
gets lost, she
will find it."

Then the men
looked at Mr. Long.

"We will go back
to the zoo now, Mr.
Long," they said.

Mr. Long went on his way.

Moonbeam looked after him.

"You will see your big friend soon," said Scott.

"And now, Moon Chimp, can you find your way back to work?" said Dr. Jim.

"Hoon!" said Moonbeam, and away she went.

Vocabulary

The total vocabulary of this book is 96 words, excluding proper names and sound words. The 39 words in roman type should be familiar to children reading on a primer level. The 16 words above primer level are shown in italic type. The number indicates the page on which the word first appears.

after   10
all   9
alone   9
asked   8
at   5

back   21
be   5
But   6

came   16
chimp   5
coming   38
could   9

doing   38

far   23
fast   31
Friend   10
from   42

get   7
going   6
got   24

had   16
help   6
her   7
him   16

if   22

know   10

laughed   16
let   49
looking   5
lost   22

men   5
moon   6

No   9
Now   13

of   11
other   9
out   10

running   33

someone   48
something   16
Soon   6
stopped   12

That   9
Then   7
There   6
trees   34
trouble   7
two   10

was   16
way   7
were   12
when   22
work   5

your   18

zoo   12